HOW TO DRAW CARTOON

ALIENS
ROBOTS &
SPACE MONSTERS

Matthew Luhn

Since 1889
GENERAL'S®
ART PRESS
Redwood City, California

For
My Dad

How to Draw Cartoon Aliens, Robots, and Space Monsters
Copyright © 2013 by Matthew Luhn

Publisher:
General's® Art Press, LLC.
Distributed by General Pencil Company, Inc.
PO Box 5311
Redwood City, CA 94063
www.GeneralPencil.com

ISBN-13: 978-0-9823671-5-5
ISBN-10: 0-9823671-5-5

Book Design and Story: Matthew Luhn
Editor: Katie W. Vanoncini
Printed in the United States of America

General's® Art Press is committed to the preservation of
our environment. Our books are printed in the USA, using
soy based inks, in a certified green printing facility.

Contents!

Draw directly onto the pages! Each section includes imagination building projects, in addition to fun how to draw step-by-step lessons!

Can you draw a picture
of where your planet
Earth is located ?

This is how you draw me, using shapes, expressions, and color!

1 First, draw an oval on a circle.

2 Add my eyes, nose, and mouth.

3 Draw my arms, gloves, and collar.

4 Now include my legs, boots, and belt.

5 Add my antennas and details.

6 Have fun coloring me in!

4

What do you look like?
Draw a step-by-step of YOU, using shapes, expressions, and color!

1 Draw a circle for your head.

2 Add your eyes, nose, and mouth.

3 Next draw your body.

4 Now include your arms.

5 Draw in your legs.

6 Have fun coloring yourself in!

Aliens and Earthlings have very similar expressions.

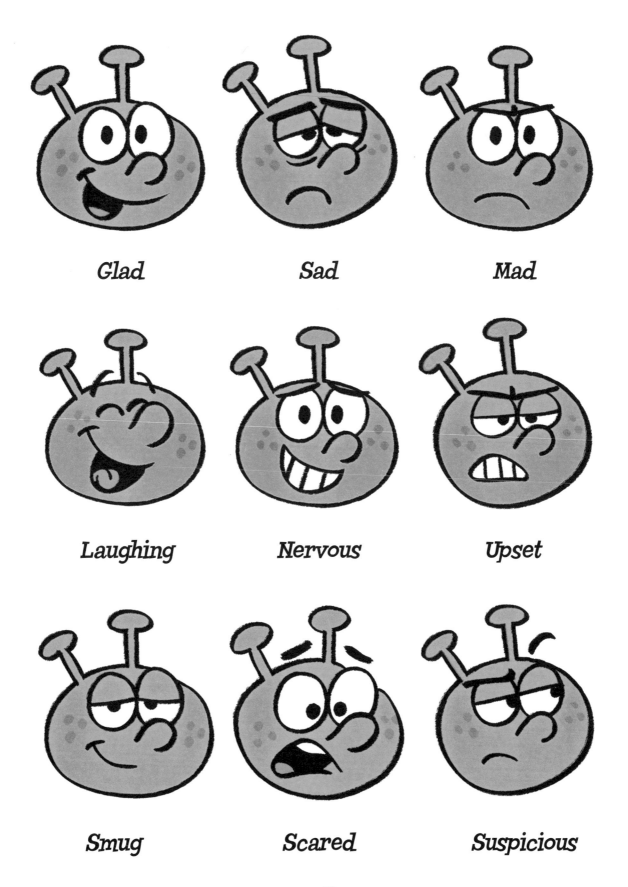

Glad   Sad   Mad

Laughing   Nervous   Upset

Smug   Scared   Suspicious

Draw nine faces of yourself with these expressions.

Glad   Sad   Mad

Laughing   Nervous   Upset

Smug   Scared   Suspicious

The inhabitants of my planet are aliens, and we come in many shapes and sizes. We may look different, but we all have antennas and friendly personalities.

Using the shapes below, create five aliens using antennas and eyes!

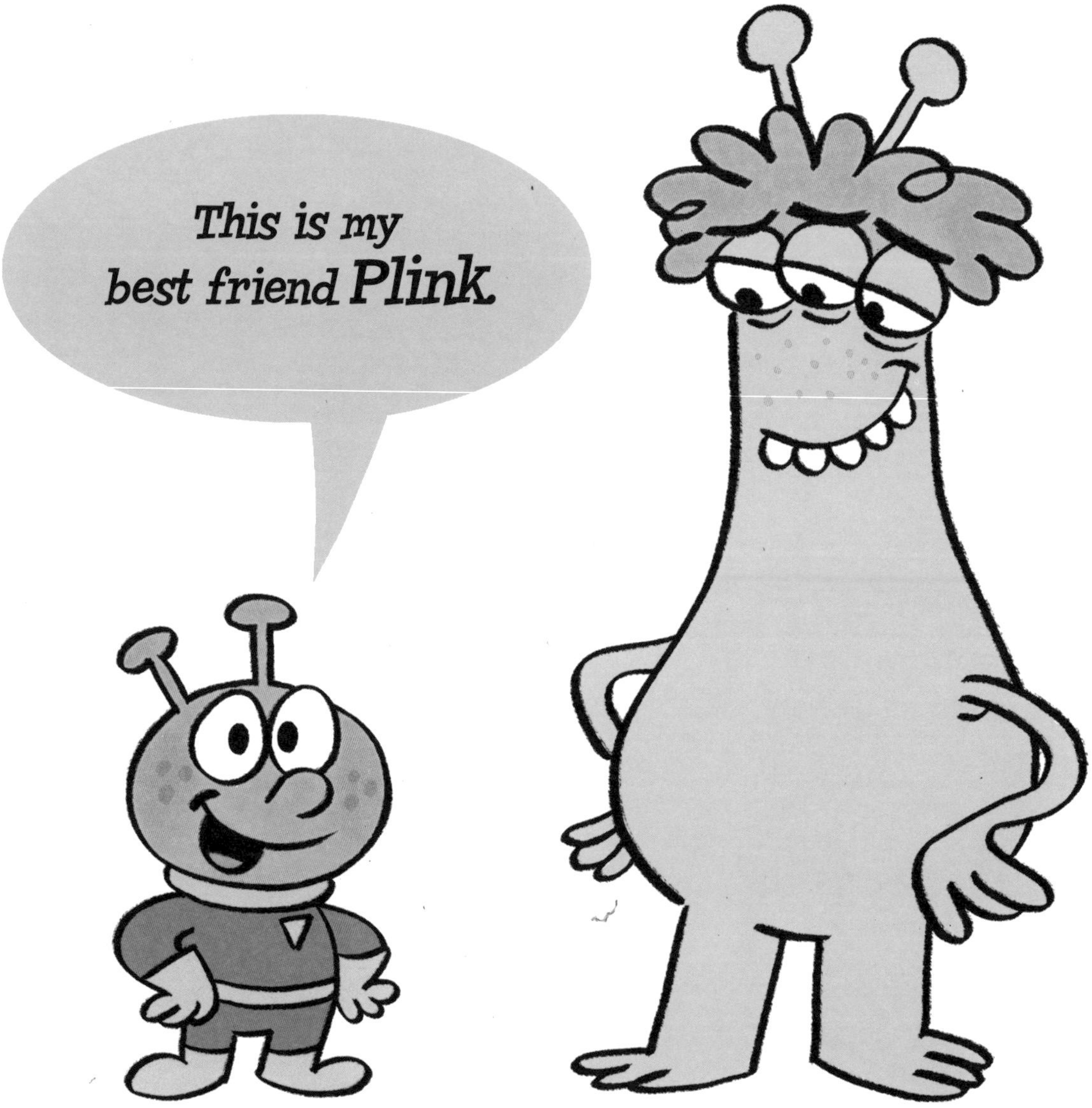
This is my best friend Plink.

How to draw Plink using shapes, expressions, and color!

1 First, draw a bean type shape.

2 Add in his eyes and mouth.

3 Draw in his legs.

4 Now include his arms.

5 Add his antennas and hair.

6 Have fun coloring in Plink!

11

I have lots of friends on my planet!

Slapfizz

Pinchy

Philwap

Flapwinger

Draw a picture of
your friends.

How to draw Slapfizz using shapes, expressions, and color!

1 First, draw half an oval.

2 Add eyes, a mouth and teeth.

3 Draw in his legs.

4 Now include his arms.

5 Add his tongue and antennas.

6 Have fun coloring in Slapfizz!

How to draw Pinchy using shapes, expressions, and color!

1 First, draw a ghost shape.

2 Add her three eyes.

3 Draw in her lips.

4 Now include her arms.

5 Add her legs and antennas.

6 Have fun coloring in Pinchy!

How to draw Philwap using shapes, expressions, and color!

1 First, draw a peanut shape.

2 Add three oval eyes.

3 Draw in his smile and teeth.

4 Now include his arms and legs.

5 Add his hair and antennas.

6 Have fun coloring in Philwap!

How to draw Flapwinger using shapes, expressions, and color!

1 Draw an egg shape on an oval.

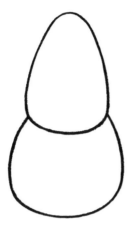

2 Add in his eyes, nose, and mouth.

3 Draw in his wings and hands.

4 Now include his legs and scales.

5 Add his ears, antenna, and tail.

6 Have fun coloring in Flapwinger!

Using your imagination,
draw two different things
that could be chasing
Philwap.

Using your creativity, draw two things Pinchy could be pinching with her claw.

Draw a picture of
what you like to do
for fun!

We also go to school on my planet.
We just hook up our thinking caps
and the information is effortlessly
fed into our heads.

Draw a picture of
what school is like
on your planet.

These are my teachers at alien school.

Math

History

Physical Education

Science

Draw a picture of
your favorite teacher.

How to draw my History teacher using shapes, expressions, and color!

1 First, draw an oval on a circle.   **2** Add his face and collar.

3 Draw his hands, arms, and shirt.   **4** Now include his legs.

5 Add his antenna, horn, and hair.   **6** Have fun coloring in my teacher!

How to draw my Science teacher using shapes, expressions, and color!

1 First, draw an oval on an oval.　**2** Add her face.

3 Draw in her tentacles.　**4** Now include her legs and shirt.

5 Add her antennas, ears, and hair.　**6** Have fun coloring in my teacher!

How to draw my P.E. teacher using shapes, expressions, and color!

1 First, draw a rectangular shape.

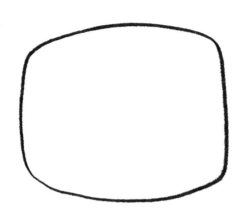

2 Add his face and horns.

3 Draw in his arms and shirt.

4 Now include his legs and pants.

5 Add his antennas and hair.

6 Have fun coloring in my teacher!

How to draw my Math teacher using shapes, expressions, and color!

1 First, draw a big oval.

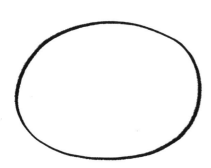

2 Add his head and face.

3 Draw in his arms and shirt.

4 Now include his pants and legs.

5 Add horns, papers, and antenna.

6 Have fun coloring in my teacher!

Have fun drawing yourself flying in my spaceship!

How to draw a spaceship using shapes, details, and color!

1 First, draw an oval.

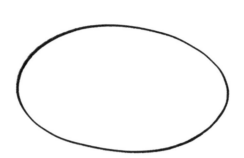

2 Add the dome window shield.

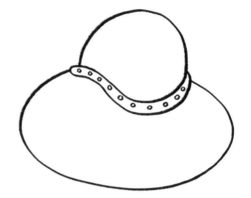

3 Draw in the wings.

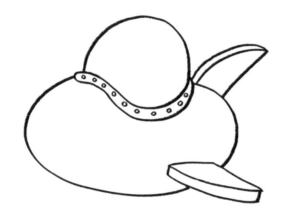

4 Now include the laser shooter.

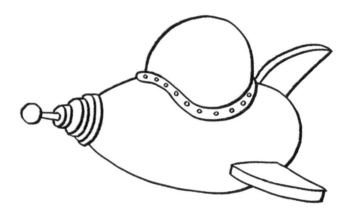

5 Add the engines and details.

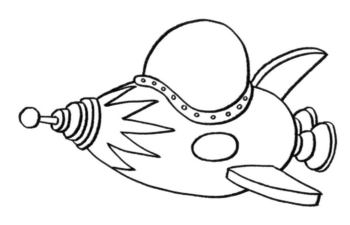

6 Have fun coloring in the spaceship!

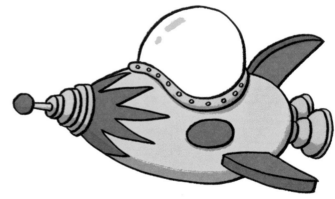

How to draw a spaceship using shapes, details, and color!

1 First, draw a long cone shape.

2 Add the center of the cone.

3 Draw in the dome window shield.

4 Now include the wings.

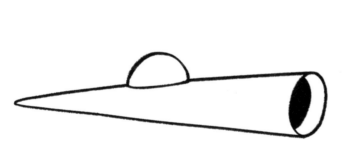

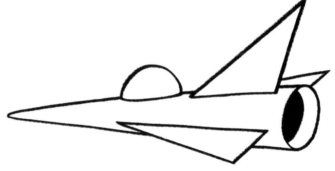

5 Add the windows and details.

6 Have fun coloring in the spaceship!

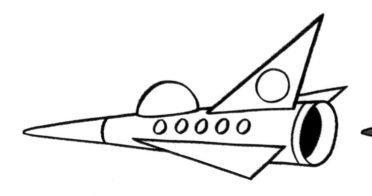

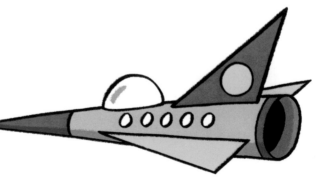

How to draw a spaceship using shapes, details, and color!

1 First, draw a long oval shape.　**2** Add the window dome and nose cap.

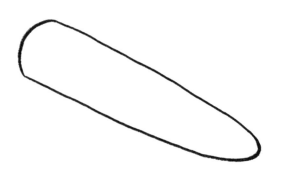
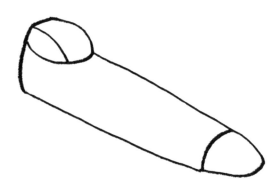

3 Using cylinders, draw the engines.　**4** Now include the wings.

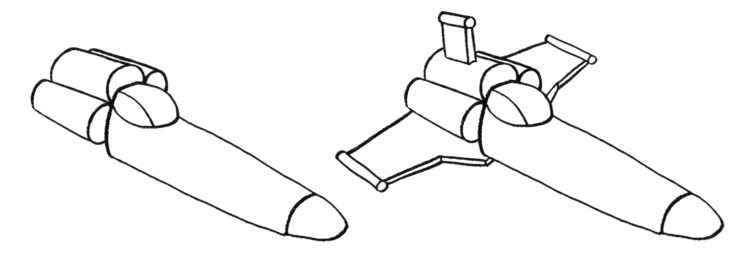

5 Add the stripes and details.　**6** Have fun coloring in the spaceship!

How to draw a spaceship using shapes, details, and color!

1 First, draw an oval shape.

2 Add the dome window shield.

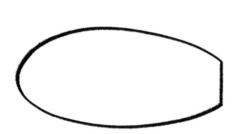

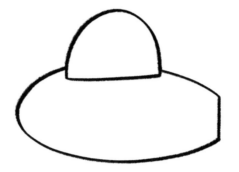

3 Draw in the tail of the ship.

4 Include the engine and wings.

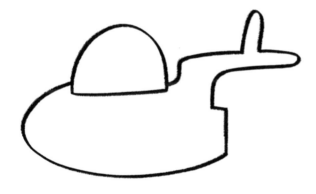

5 Add the radar and other details.

6 Have fun coloring in the spaceship!

35

How to draw a spaceship using shapes, details, and color!

1 First, draw a long cone shape.

2 Add the window dome and cylinders.

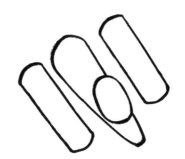

3 Complete the rocket boosters.

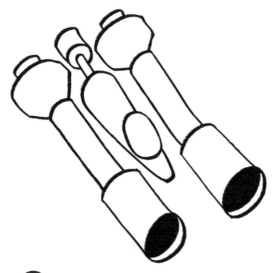

4 Now include the wings and lasers.

5 Add the stripes and details.

6 Have fun coloring in the spaceship!

How to draw a spaceship using shapes, details, and color!

1 Draw a loaf of bread type shape.

2 Add the window dome on top.

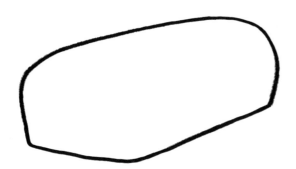

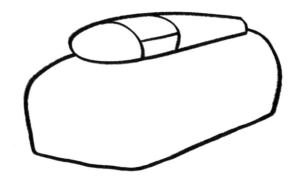

3 Include the tail fin using triangles.

4 Draw cylinders for rocket boosters.

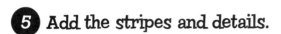

5 Add the stripes and details.

6 Have fun coloring in the spaceship!

Using the shapes below, create four
spaceships using your imagination!

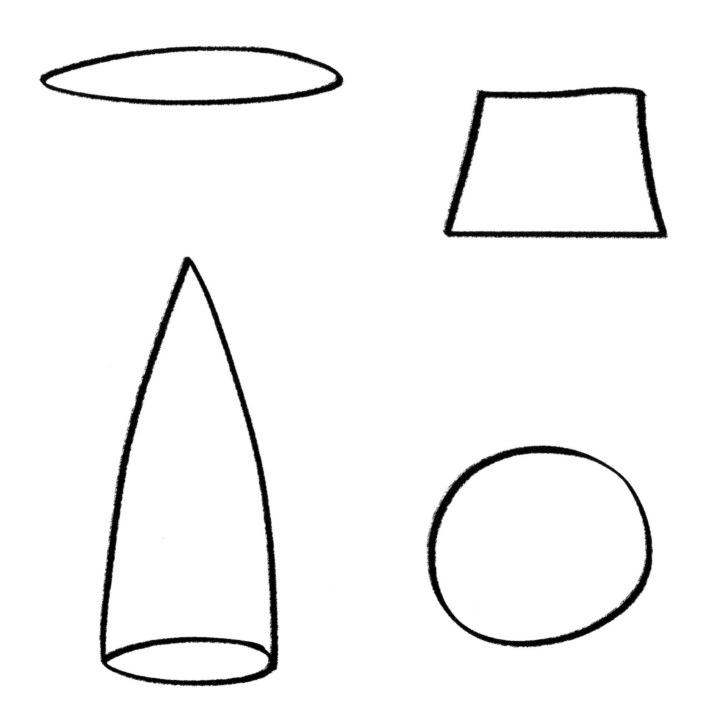

Let's race!
Draw you in your spaceship
racing other spaceships!

41

The trick to drawing robots is to imagine their bodies made up of metal cylinders, spheres, cubes, and hoses. Once you have the body completed you can give them a cartoony face.

Using the shapes below, create four robots
with hose arms and metal bodies!

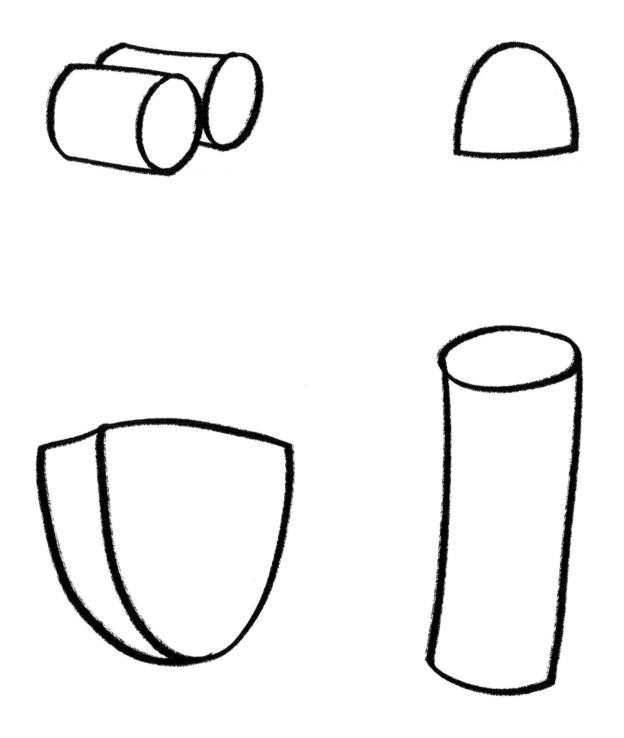

How to draw Zips using shapes, expressions, and color!

1 First, draw an oval and cylinder.

2 Add the face and jaw.

3 Draw in the arms and neck.

4 Now include the hips and legs.

5 Add the antenna and details.

6 Have fun coloring in Zips!

44

How to draw Lenbot using shapes, expressions, and color!

1 Draw a long cube and cylinder.　**2** Add eyes and a neck.

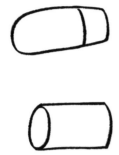

3 Draw in his arms and hands.　**4** Now include his legs and feet.

5 Add his antennas and dials.　**6** Have fun coloring in Lenbot!

How to draw Blip using shapes, expressions, and color!

1 First, draw half a sphere.

2 Add a head, mouth, and collar.

3 Draw in the arms.

4 Now include the legs.

5 Add the antennas and details.

6 Have fun coloring in Blip!

How to draw Lug using shapes, expressions, and color!

1 Draw half an oval and square.

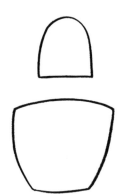

2 Add the face and neck.

3 Draw in the arms.

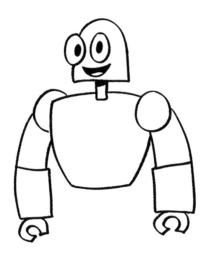

4 Now include the legs.

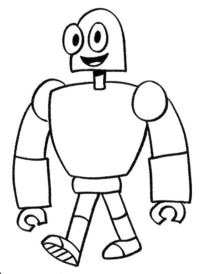

5 Add the antenna and details.

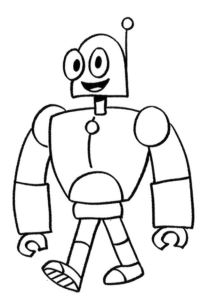

6 Have fun coloring in Lug!

How to draw Torrg using shapes, expressions, and color!

1 Draw a circle and hexagon head.   **2** Add eyes, a mouth, and waist.

3 Draw in the shoulders and arms.   **4** Now include the legs and feet.

5 Add hands and details.   **6** Have fun coloring in Torrg!

How to draw Raybot using shapes, expressions, and color!

1 First, draw half of an egg shape.

2 Add a rectangle for the head.

3 Complete the head and neck.

4 Now include the face.

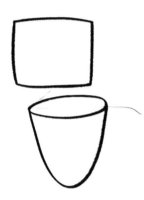

5 Add the antenna and details.

6 Have fun coloring in Raybot!

49

Using your imagination,
draw what is surprising
the robot!

On this page, draw two things the robot wants to eat.

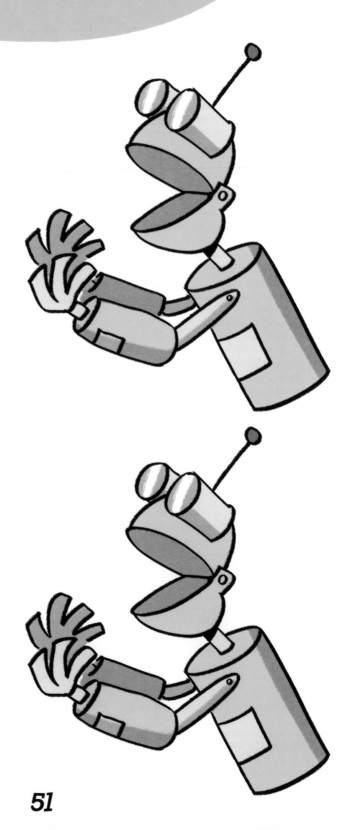

Draw one big robot using the shapes
on the opposite page. Have fun adding in the
extra details to show your style!

Space monsters are a big problem on my planet.
They have sharp teeth, claws, and very bad tempers.
When it comes to drawing these monsters, you can
use any shape imaginable.

Using the shapes below, draw fangs, horns, claws, and evil eyes to create five space monsters!

How to draw a space monster using shapes, expressions, and color!

1 First, draw a curved raindrop.

2 Add an eye, nostrils, and mouth.

3 Draw the front arms.

4 Now include the legs and spikes.

5 Add antennas and wings.

6 Color in your space monster!

How to draw a space monster using shapes, expressions, and color!

1 First, draw a snake shape.

2 Add an oval head.

3 Draw in the eyes.

4 Now include a smile.

5 Add antennas and wings.

6 Color in your space monster!

59

How to draw a Martian Emperor using shapes, expressions, and color!

1 First, draw a ghost-shape.

2 Add the eyes and mouth.

3 Draw an oval shape for the body.

4 Now include the arms and legs.

5 Add antennas, crown, and cape.

6 Color in the Martian Emperor!

How to draw a space monster using shapes, expressions, and color!

1 First, draw a peanut shape.

2 Add the eyes and mouth.

3 Draw in the arms.

4 Now include legs.

5 Add antenna and wings.

6 Color in your space monster!

How to draw a space monster using shapes, expressions, and color!

1 First, draw an oval.

2 Add the eyes.

3 Draw in the mouth and teeth.

4 Now include arms and legs.

5 Add antennas and tongue.

6 Color in your space monster!

How to draw a space monster using shapes, expressions, and color!

1 First, draw an oval.

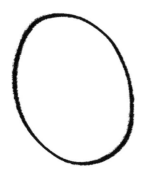

2 Add the eye and mouth.

3 Draw in the tentacles.

4 Now include the legs.

5 Add an antenna and wings.

6 Color in your space monster!

Add bodies, claws, and anything else you would like to complete these space monsters!

Draw more space monsters!

Robots are also great for vacuuming
up space monsters!

Using your imagination,
draw what's pulling
the monster's tongue.

On this page, draw what's pulling the monster's tentacles.

Draw a giant battle
between the robots and
the space monsters!

For your courage and cartoon skills, you've been awarded the alien medal of "Hero!" Congratulations!

Draw a picture of
yourself proudly
wearing the medal!